FIRST VIOLIN

BOOK IV   VIOLIN PART

THE ASSOCIATED BOARD OF THE ROYAL SCHOOLS OF MUSIC

Allegro
from Sonata in F

HANDEL, Op. 1 No. 12

All dynamics, phrasing, bowing and fingering are editorial.

© 1970 by The Associated Board of the Royal Schools of Music

Giga
from Concert Sonata

VERACINI, Op.2 No.8

Scherzo & Trio
from Sonata in C minor

BEETHOVEN, Op.30 No.2

The original bowing is shown in the pianoforte part. The violin part contains some additional editorial suggestions.

Menuet
from 'Bunte Reihe'

DAVID, Op.30 No.15

Un poco allegretto

Romantic Piece

DVORAK, Op.75 No.1

Orientale

CUI, Op.50 No.9

Berceuse

FAURÉ, Op.16

Nocturne

LILI BOULANGER

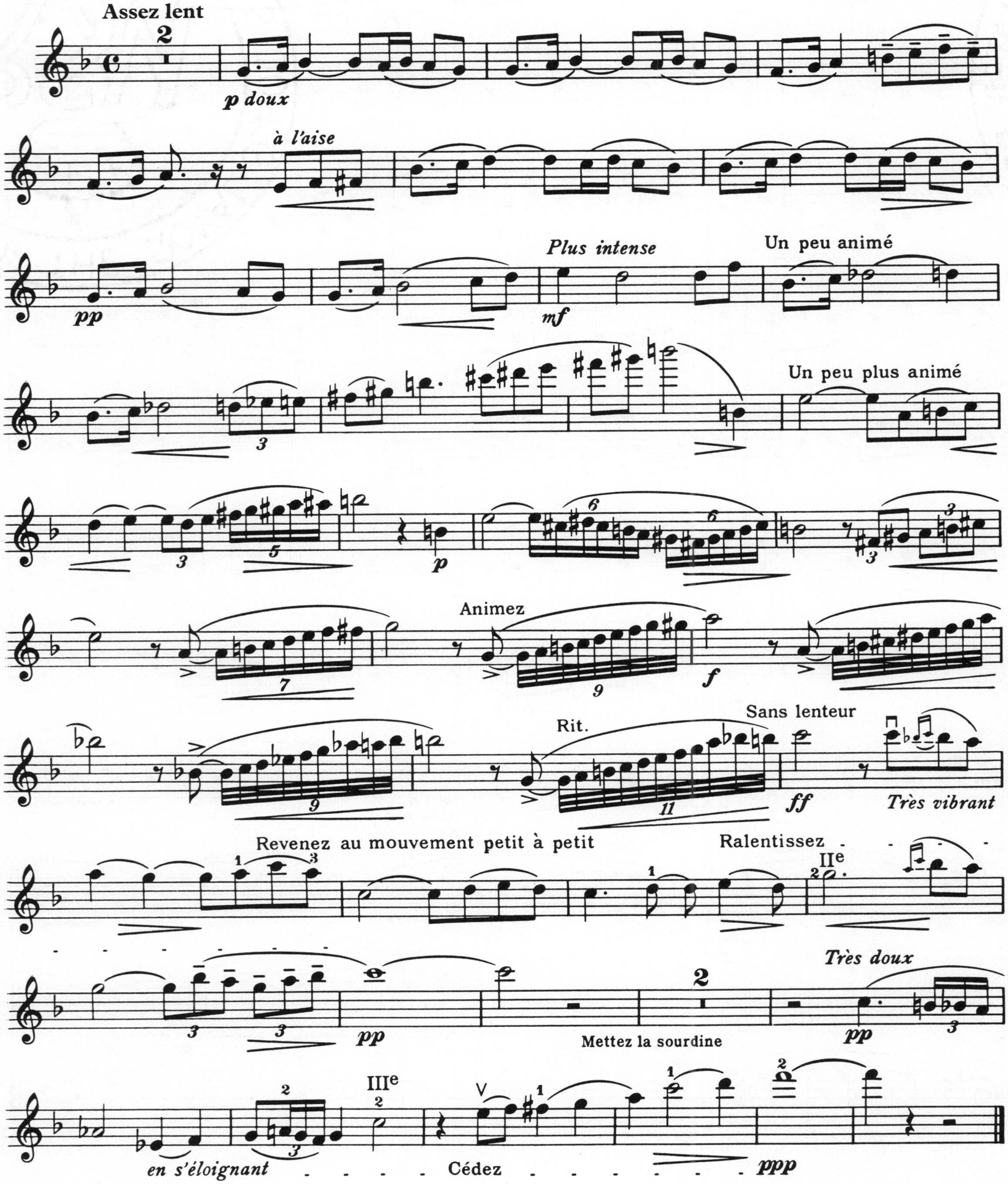

Slow Air

Rather slow, with gentle feeling

HERBERT HOWELLS

A. B. 202

AB 1775

Printed in England by Caligraving Limited, Thetford, Norfolk

5:02

FIRST VIOLIN

BOOK IV

THE ASSOCIATED BOARD OF THE ROYAL SCHOOLS OF MUSIC

Allegro
from Sonata in F

HANDEL, Op. 1 No. 12

All dynamics, phrasing, bowing and fingering are editorial.

Giga
from Concert Sonata

VERACINI, Op.2 No.8

Scherzo & Trio
from Sonata in C minor

BEETHOVEN, Op.30 No.2

The original bowing is shown in the pianoforte part. The violin part contains some additional editorial suggestions.

Scherzo da Capo

Menuet
from 'Bunte Reihe'

DAVID, Op.30 No.15

Un poco animato

Tempo I

Romantic Piece

DVOŘÁK, Op.75 No.1

Poco meno mosso

Ped. sin al Fine

Orientale

CUI, Op.50 No.9

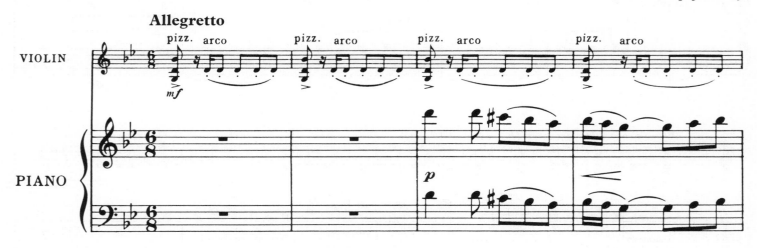

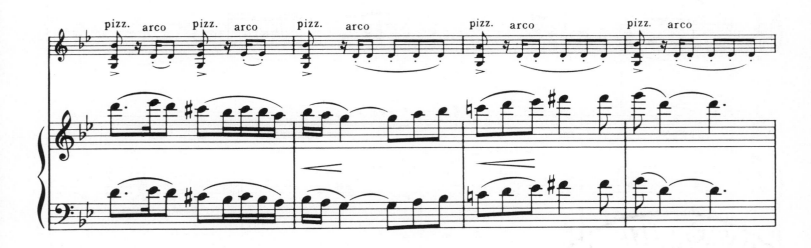

Berceuse

FAURÉ, Op.16

26

Nocturne

LILI BOULANGER

Slow Air

HERBERT HOWELLS

AB 1775

Printed in England by Caligraving Limited, Thetford, Norfolk